A a

apple

Say the name of each picture. Color the things that begin with the same sound as apple.

Trace **A** and **a**.

A A A a a a

B b

bike

Say the name of each picture. Color the things that begin with the same sound as bike.

Trace **B** and **b**.

B B B b b b

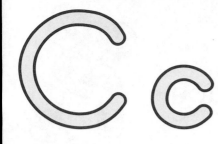 C c

cat

Say the name of each picture. Circle the things that begin with the same sound as cat.

Trace **C** and **c**.

C C C c c c

D d

dog

Say the name of each picture. Color the things that begin with the same sound as dog.

Trace **D** and **d**.

D D D d d d

Draw a line to connect each letter to the picture whose name begins with that letter sound.

A a

B b

C c

D d

E e

eggs

Say the name of each picture. Circle the things that begin with the same sound as eggs.

Trace **E** and **e**.

E E E e e e

F f

fish

Say the name of each picture. Color the things that begin with the same sound as fish.

Trace **F** and **f**.

F F F f f f

G g

GOOD JOB!

goat

Say the name of each picture. Circle the things that begin with the same sound as goat.

Trace **G** and **g**.

G G G   g g g

H h

house

Say the name of each picture. Color the things that begin with the same sound as house.

Trace **H** and **h**.

Draw a line to connect each letter to the picture whose name begins with that letter sound.

E e

F f

G g

H h

I i

igloo

Say the name of each picture. Circle the things that begin with the same sound as igloo.

INK

Trace **I** and **i**.

I I I   i i i

11

J j

jar

Say the name of each picture. Color the things that begin with the same sound as jar.

Trace **J** and **j**.

J J J j j j

K k

key

Say the name of each picture. Circle the things that begin with the same sound as key.

Trace **K** and **k**.

K K K k k k

L l

lamp

Say the name of each picture. Color the things that begin with the same sound as lamp.

Trace **L** and **l**.

Connect the letters in ABC order to find something whose name begins with the **L** sound.

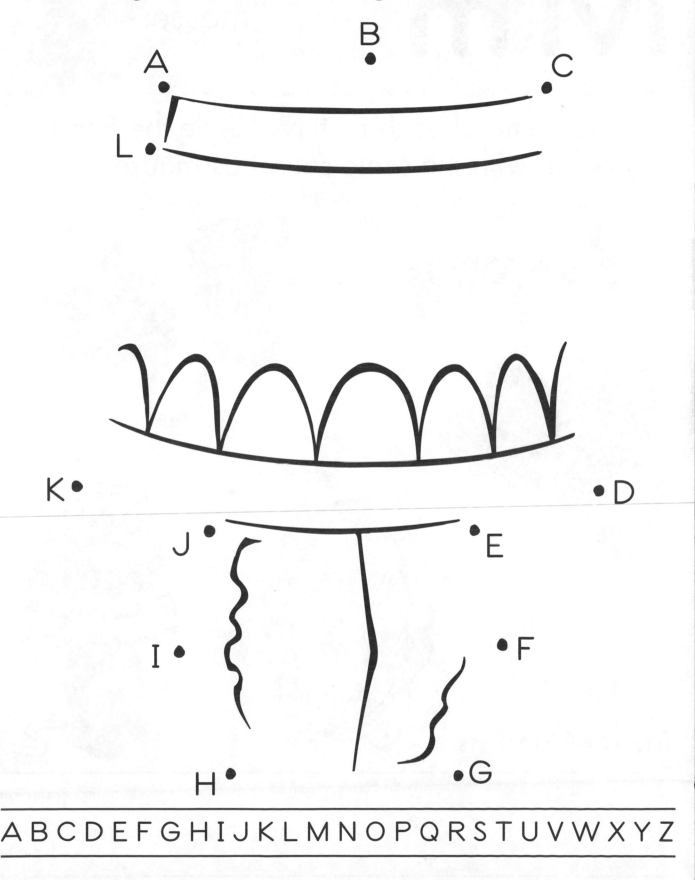

A B C D E F G H I J K L M N O P Q R S T U V W X Y Z

M m

mouse

Say the name of each picture. Circle the things that begin with the same sound as mouse.

Trace **M** and **m**.

M M m m

N n

nut

Say the name of each picture. Color the things that begin with the same sound as nut.

Trace **N** and **n**.

N N N N n n n

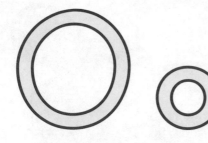 

octopus

Say the name of each picture. Circle the things that begin with the same sound as octopus.

Trace **O** and **o**.

P p

pig

Say the name of each picture. Color the things that begin with the same sound as pig.

Trace **P** and **p**.

P P P

p p p

Connect the letters in ABC order to find something whose name begins with the **P** sound.

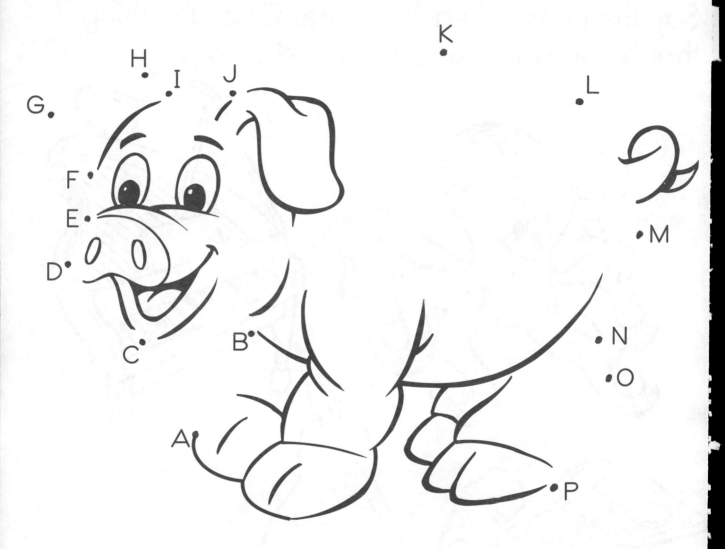

A B C D E F G H I J K L M N O P Q R S T U V W X Y Z

Q q

quarter

Say the name of each picture. Circle the things that begin with the same sound as **q**uarter.

Trace **Q** and **q**.

Q Q Q q q q

R r

ring

Say the name of each picture. Color the things that begin with the same sound as ring.

Trace **R** and **r**.

R R R r r r

S s  sun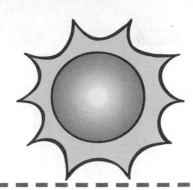

Say the name of each picture. Circle the things that begin with the same sound as sun.

Trace **S** and **s**.

S S S s s s

T t

tent

Say the name of each picture. Color the things that begin with the same sound as tent.

Trace **T** and **t**.

T T T T t t t t

Connect the letters in ABC order to find something that has a name beginning with the **T** sound.

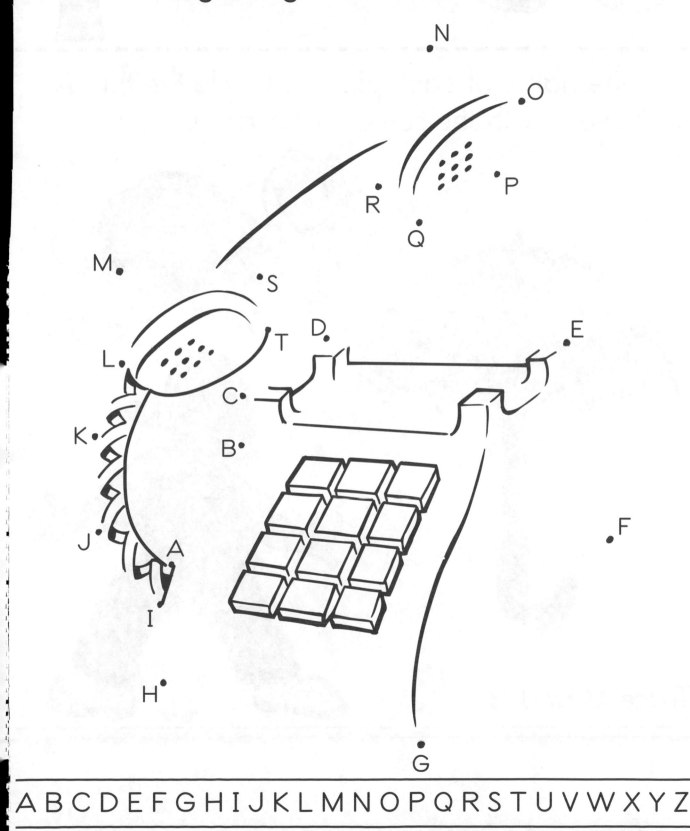

A B C D E F G H I J K L M N O P Q R S T U V W X Y Z

U u

up

Say the name of each picture. Circle the things that begin with the same sound as up.

Trace **U** and **u**.

U U U U u u u

V v

vest

Say the name of each picture. Color the things that begin with the same sound as vest.

I LOVE YOU!

Trace **V** and **v**.

V V V V V V

W w

web

Say the name of each picture. Circle the things that begin with the same sound as web.

Trace **W** and **w**.

W W w w

X x  X-ray

Trace **X** and **x**. Circle the X-ray.

X X X x x x

Y y  yarn

Trace **Y** and **y**. Color the yak.

Y Y Y y y y

Z z

zipper

Say the name of each picture. Color the things that begin with the same sound as zipper.

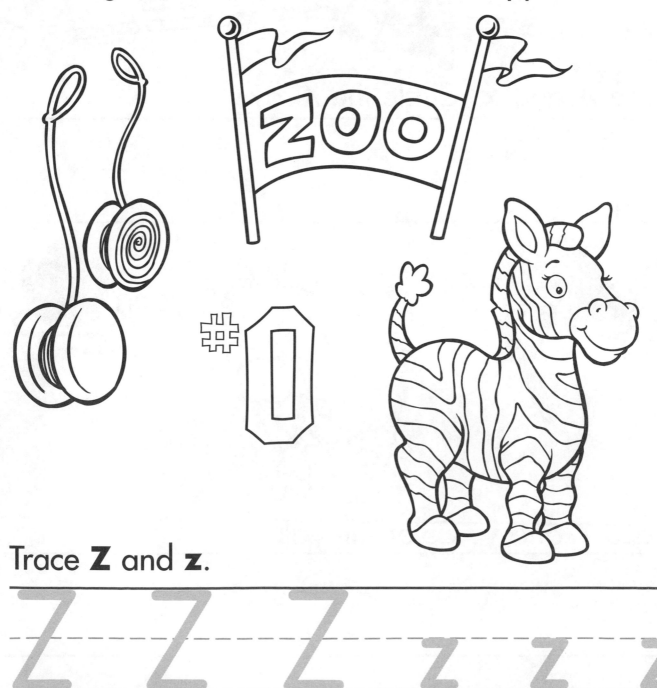

Trace **Z** and **z**.

Z Z Z z z z

Connect the letters in ABC order to find some whose name begins with the **Z** sound.

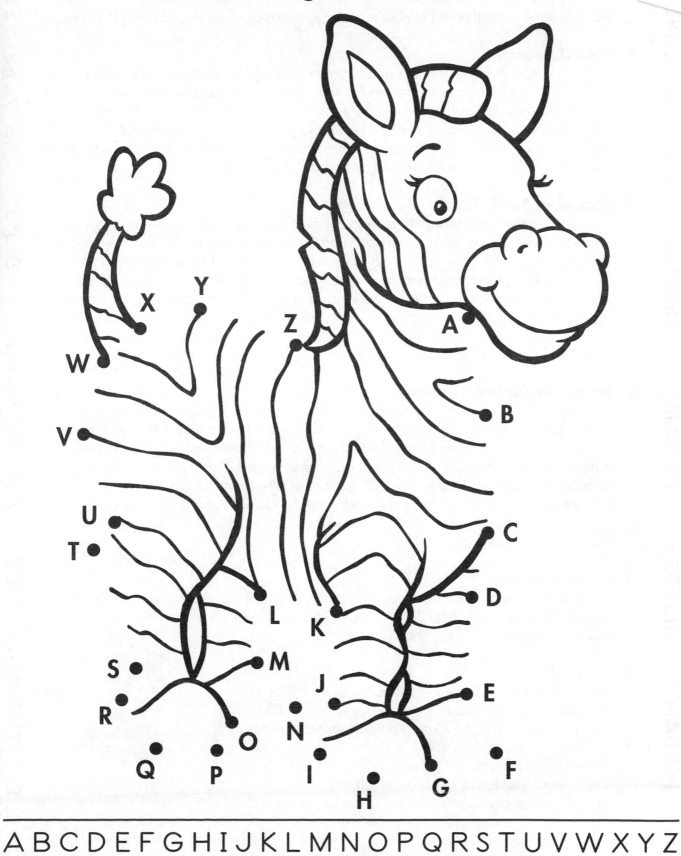

A B C D E F G H I J K L M N O P Q R S T U V W X Y Z

Family Fun Activities

The following activities will review the concepts explored on the workbook pages.

1. Sound Search

As you go about your daily activities with the child, play an alphabet sound search game. Tell the child you are looking for something that begins with a specific sound and let the child guess until your selected item is identified. For example, as you stand in line at the grocery store, tell the child you see something that begins with the "L" sound. Let the child guess until the lettuce in your basket is correctly guessed. Take turns and let the child ask you to find a specific object.

2. Alphabet Flash Cards

Use inexpensive index cards to create alphabet flash cards. Print an uppercase alphabet letter on one side of the card and the corresponding lowercase letter on the back. If your child wants to print the cards, encourage him or her to do so. Hold up a completed card and ask the child to name the letter and say the sound associated with it. Expect the child to learn one or two letters each time you play. Let the child practice sequencing the alphabet letters by placing them in ABC order. Practice with the uppercase letter side of the cards until they are familiar to the child, and then turn the cards over and review the lowercase letters.

3. Make an Alphabet Book

Staple together 26 pages of blank paper. Encourage the child to write an upper- and lowercase letter pair on each page. Ask the child to name each letter and tell you the sound associated with it. Help the child search through magazines and cut out pictures of objects that begin with each letter sound. Do not expect the child to complete the alphabet pages in order or in one sitting. Instead, consider this a long-term project and add a letter page each time the child becomes familiar with the sound and printing of the letter. To review the letter sounds, ask the child to "read" the book to you often.

4. Make Letters

Using play dough, ask the child to create letters of the alphabet and name the sound associated with each letter. Begin with uppercase letters and advance to lowercase letters when the child is ready.

5. Letter Day

Plan a "letter day." Choose a letter. Write it on a card and give it to the child. During the day, ask the child to look for, and name, things that begin with that letter sound.

6. Reward Stickers

Use reward stickers to celebrate a job well done. You or the child can choose when to place a sticker on a specific page. Use a sticker as a reward when the child completes a page that requires extra care or is a little more difficult. The child can choose to place stickers on pages he or she is proud of completing.